Disney

Winnie the Pooh

Piglet's Night-Lights

• Book Seven •

Disney PRESS
New York

Copyright © 2009 Disney Enterprises, Inc. Based on the "Winnie the Pooh" works, by A. A. Milne and E. H. Shepard. All Rights Reserved.

"Piglet's Night-Lights"adapted from the book *Piglet's Night Light.*
Copyright © 2003 Disney Enterprises, Inc.

All rights reserved. Published by Disney Press, an imprint of Disney Book Group.
No part of this book may be reproduced or transmitted in any form or by any means, electronic or mechanical, including photocopying, recording, or by any information storage and retrieval system, without written permission from the publisher.
For information address Disney Press, 114 Fifth Avenue, New York, New York 10011-5690

Printed in China

First Edition
10 9 8 7 6 5 4 3 2 1

Library of Congress Catalog Card Number on file.

ISBN 978-1-4231-2561-7

For more Disney Press fun,
visit www.disneybooks.com

It was twilight in the Hundred-Acre Wood when Winnie the Pooh knocked on his friend Piglet's door. "Ready for our campout, Piglet?" he asked.

"Are you quite sure about this, Pooh?" said Piglet anxiously. "It's getting awfully dark. Maybe we could just camp out here in my living room."

"That would be a camp-*in*, not a camp-*out*," said Pooh.

Pooh came inside to help Piglet get ready.

"I have the feeling I'm forgetting something," Piglet said as he packed his teddy bear.

"Well, let's see," said Pooh. "We have honey." He patted the honeypot in his backpack. "And we have plenty of muffins." Just to be sure, Pooh tucked two more next to Piglet's teddy bear. "What else could we possibly need for our campout?"

So Pooh and Piglet set off, but as they walked, it grew darker and darker.

"What's that?" Piglet asked, pointing to two eyes staring at them from a high tree.

"I don't know," Pooh replied, shivering.

"Why, it's me—Owl," the eyes answered. "I thought you two might need help finding the others. We owls can see quite well at night, you know."

"Oh, thank you, Owl!" said Piglet with a big sigh of relief.

By the time the friends reached the campsite, it was completely dark. Pooh bumped right into Rabbit, who was struggling to put up the tent.

"Well, don't just stand there," Rabbit snapped. "I need all the help I can get!"

"Did I hear someone say 'help'?" Tigger called, bouncing into the clearing. "Have no fear, Tigger's here—with illuminagination!" And he proudly held up a lantern.

"Oh, and you brought a light, too!" cried Piglet. "Thank goodness—it's *awfully* dark out here."

With the help of Tigger's lantern, the friends set up the tent. Then Piglet climbed inside and began to unpack.

"Oh, no!" he whimpered, climbing out a few minutes later. "I forgot my night-light! I can't sleep without one. What am I going to do?"

"Don't worry, Buddy Boy," said Tigger. "You can use my lantern!" But just then, the lantern flickered out. "On second thought," said Tigger, "Long Ears must have something in there you can use."

Tigger dove into the tent and pulled out a kite, a ball, and several pots and pans. At last, he spotted a flashlight. He tried to turn it on. "This thingamabob's not working either!" he cried when nothing happened.

Just then, there was a crash in the nearby bushes. "Look who's here!" Pooh exclaimed as Eeyore walked up.

Eeyore looked around the campsite. "Can't have a campout without a campfire," he said.

Of course, everyone agreed.

So they gathered up some sticks, and a few minutes later a beautiful fire was burning.

"Campfires certainly are pleasant," Piglet said. "They make a very good sort of light."

"They do a fantalicious job cooking marshy-mallows, too!" Tigger cried.

Rabbit rubbed his chin and thought about it for a minute. "Fire is fine," he said at last. "But I think sunlight is the best light of all. It makes the vegetables in my garden grow big and tasty—with my help, of course."

Pooh rubbed his belly and nodded. "I like the way the sun warms my tummy when I lie in the grass," he said. "Especially when my tummy's full of honey!"

"And don't forget the colors the sun makes at sunset," Piglet added with a sigh. "They're simply splendid!"

Rabbit, Pooh, and Piglet continued to daydream until they were suddenly interrupted by their bouncy buddy, Tigger. He had something he wanted to show them.

"Hey, look everyone!" exclaimed Tigger. "Is that a s-s-s-snake on the side of the tent?"

"That looks like your tail to me," said Rabbit.

Tigger looked at the tent more closely. "Well, what do you know!" he said.

Then Rabbit put his thumbs together and fluttered his hands like butterfly wings. "Guess what this is?" he asked.

Tigger and Owl looked at the tent and the shape fluttering across it.

"Why, it's a shadow puppet!" declared Owl. "It looks just like a butterfly."

"Tiggers *like* shadow puppets!" said Tigger.

And Pooh and his friends played shadow puppets until it was time to go to sleep.

"Shall we go to bed now?" Pooh asked Piglet, with a yawn and a big stretch.

But Piglet shook his head. "I can't sleep without a night-light, Pooh," he replied sadly.

Pooh tapped his forehead to wake up any ideas that might be there. "Think, think, think," he muttered. Then he looked up at the sky. "There are night-lights, Piglet!" he said, pointing up at the twinkling stars. "I've never seen so many of them!"

Just then a little firefly landed right between Pooh's eyes. Pooh tumbled back off the log he was sitting on. "And the fireflies are night-lights, too." He laughed.

Piglet looked around. "You're right, Pooh!" he exclaimed. "There are night-lights everywhere!" Then he pointed to the moon.

"Look how bright the moon is tonight. It's even brighter than my own night-light." He smiled at his friend. "I feel much better, Pooh Bear. Thank you."

"Do you think you might be able to sleep now, Piglet?" Pooh asked, with another big yawn.

But Piglet didn't answer. He was curled up on the hollow log, already fast asleep.

Y0-CDJ-757

Ready-Set-RN™

uthor:
lia W. Aucoin,
NS, RN, BC
ssistant Professor
niversity of
orth Carolina
Greensboro
onsultant
ursing Professional
evelopment

ontributor:
arbara Kuhn Timby,
NC, MA
ursing Professor
len Oaks
ommunity College

ditor:
eslie Treas, RN,
hD(c), MSN, CNNP
irector, Research
nd Development
ssessment
echnologies
nstitute®, LLC

ll rights reserved. Printed the United States of merica. No part of this ook shall be reproduced, ored in a retrieval stem, or transmitted any means, electronic, echanical, photocopying, cording, or otherwise, ithout written permission om the publisher. opyright© Assessment echnologies Institute®, LLC 006. NCLEX-RN® a registered trademark the National Council State Boards of Nursing, ic. and, as such, use the trademark is not onsidered an endorsement this book.

Table of Contents

Ready-Set-Registered Nurse Preparing for the NCLEX-RN®

Whether you have always wanted to be a nurse, or this is an exciting second career choice, you have been working hard for some time in a nursing program. However, once you graduate, you still have to pass the NCLEX-RN®. This should be easy after all you have been through, yet it can be a challenge. This booklet will introduce you to techniques and tips to help you prepare for this challenge. Join us as we help you get

Ready...Set...Be a Registered Nurse!

Before Graduation

Review Your Exams

When faculty offer you a test review session before or after exams, take advantage of this opportunity. Often students see the exam review as a chance to argue about bad test questions, but the value lies in the ability to see through the question to the content being emphasized. Whether as a group or individually, seek out more information about any missed items, so that the intended content can be clearly understood.

Using Your Achievement Tests

Achievement tests have been selected to serve as a validation of your application of knowledge. They also act as a guide to the faculty for improving their courses. Putting forth your best efforts on achievement tests can provide you with confidence as you approach the NCLEX-RN®. Scores for tests can be interpreted with assistance from the testing service and the faculty. Results can be used to improve your test-taking skills and to focus your study efforts on specific content areas. Take your achievement tests seriously and participate in reviewing the results.

Reading Your Textbooks

Studies indicate that most students do not read the entire assignment before class or before the test. So how can you use your textbook in the best way? Read the tables, trace through the figures and diagrams, discuss the care plans and maps, and respond to the critical-thinking questions and case studies. By doing at least this much, you can begin to zone in on pertinent information that will support your NCLEX-RN® preparation. Then, whenever you encounter a content area you need to learn more about, you can go to your textbook, class notes, and other resources in the library, hospital, or online and read the supporting text for further information.

NCLEX-RN® Test Plan

The test plan changes every three years. To download the current test plan to see the major categories of tested content and the nursing activities included, go to the National Council of

State Boards of Nursing home page at http://www.ncsbn.org. On it, you'll also find a section for candidates. Download the Candidate Bulletin (http://www.ncsbn.org/testing/candidates.asp) for very specific information on registering for and taking the NCLEX-RN®. A new bulletin is published each January.

Applying for the NCLEX-RN®

Your program will provide you with two applications–one for the NCLEX-RN® and one for licensure in your state. If you will be initially licensed by another state, you will need to complete that state's licensure process. The most accurate information about completion of the NCLEX-RN® application is in the Candidate Bulletin, which will be given to you, and can be downloaded at http://www.ncsbn.org/testing/candidates.asp.

One Month Before the NCLEX-RN®

Scheduling Options

Avoid testing during a period of stress, such as the anniversary of a parent's death, the week before your wedding, while buying a first home, or when ill. Look at your life calendar carefully when selecting your possible dates. Avoiding periods of conflicting anxiety can help you focus your attention. Consider scheduling one month before or two weeks after the wedding. Think seriously of taking your dream vacation after the test. What about waiting a month after buying that first home? Just do not overlook the importance of these stressors and their negative effects.

Too Soon or Too Late

While scheduling at the time best for you is important, studies have indicated that if you take the test too soon or too late, your success rate declines. Be sure to give yourself a month to transition from the frenzy of school. During this time, review your course materials and class notes, practice many questions, and then test. Waiting more than five months can cause your confidence to dwindle, distract you from your purpose, and confuse you. Schedule the exam within a reasonable time frame to increase your chances of success.

Set a Readiness Target

Scheduling your test for a convenient date and avoiding any stressors you can is important. However, incorporating your study plan into that scheduling decision is important too. Thus, setting a readiness target, blending the scheduled testing date with the study plan, and setting a target of one week before the test to have reached your study goals is ideal. Study content that needs review, and complete sufficient practice questions, until you achieve that feeling of readiness. Breaking down your readiness target into manageable study goals will make it easier to visualize your objective.

Complete the Tutorial

Go to the Candidate section at http://www.ncsbn.org/testing/candidate.asp and click on the tutorial. Even though you will be going through this tutorial on your test day, the more familiar you become with the NCLEX-RN® screens and processes, the easier the test can seem. If your anxiety is particularly high when you begin the actual NCLEX-RN® on test day, you can run through the tutorial a couple of times quickly (since it is familiar) to calm yourself a bit. Practice using the calculator on the computer. Those who are unfamiliar with "/" representing "divided by", and "*" representing "multiply", are slowed down.

Scheduling the Test

The race to schedule the test is often won by the person who has planned options well. While you should choose several possible dates for testing, be sure to identify and select *only* your best time of day. The day of the week can be accommodated far better than the wrong time of the day. Go to http://www.pearsonvue.com/nclex to find testing center locations. Look into the location of several testing centers and their ease of access from your home, so that you have more than one option of sites. Please note that you can test in any city or state — the testing center is not linked to your state of initial licensure. If driving to the city makes you uncomfortable, then plan to arrive a day early or choose a smaller community. Staying in the mountains or with a relative a few days before testing might do a world of good. Before making the call, have a list of sites and dates, and your preferred time of day. Scheduling can be accomplished once you have the Authorization to Test through www.vue.com/nclex.

Employer Pressure

Many employers are now very aware of the time lapse between graduation and actual licensure. You must wait for the paperwork to be sent by the school, be processed by the Board of Nursing, and forwarded to the NCSBN for the Authorization to Test to be issued. Meanwhile, employers are excitedly waiting for the onslaught of graduates to join their team. In their enthusiasm (and yours), it is likely that you are willing to accept employment between graduation and the test. This could reinforce in your mind the nursing tech role or put you back in the classroom learning the policies of the facility. However, it could be taking time away from practicing more test questions and working on areas where you need improvement. At this point, there are many positions open. While you may be the best candidate and love the workplace, you will not be of any help to the organization if you test without proper preparation.

Mirror Exercises

Even if most people in your life have been encouraging, there may be a haunting voice that tells you that you are not worthy, you are a loser, or you will never be a nurse. In times of extreme stress it's hard to ignore that voice. In order to overcome negative thoughts — the gremlins in your head — you can do mirror exercises or positive affirmations. When you say good things about yourself often enough, then you begin to believe them. To do mirror exercises, choose a phrase or set of phrases that demonstrate how wonderful you are. "I'm a good friend." "I'm a good nurse." "I graduated from the nursing program while working full time." "I love being a nurse." "I will be successful on the NCLEX-RN®." Eliminate self-doubt by repeatedly telling yourself how wonderful you are. Saying these things into a mirror adds to your conviction.

Exercise

While you have been in school you may not have been able to exercise as often as you would like. During the study period you can resume your program of exercise: walk, go to the gym, or play a team sport. This will help make your body as fit as your mind, giving you a needed outlet during days of study and a way to relieve stress in those days immediately before the test. Going to the gym immediately before or after the test can be a great way to deal with anxiety in a healthful way. When there is a break during the test, going outside and taking a brisk five-minute walk can help clear your head and help you to relax before resuming testing.

A Week Before the NCLEX-RN®

Work Schedule

If you are employed before the test, it's likely that you have been working all along. Therefore, you are organized and accustomed to studying and working at the same time. However, working 12-hour nights the week of the test will drain you. Many employers schedule graduates to be released from the work schedule during the week of testing. If you are working, and getting the week of the test off is not offered, then you should request the time off. You need it to rest, study, and focus.

How To Know You Are Ready

After you have created an effective study plan that includes focusing on necessary content and practicing test questions, you will reach a point when you will feel saturated with information. That feeling of satisfaction, is one that you should recognize. However, any haunting self-doubt can make it difficult for you to feel ready. If you have doubts, then do something to assure your readiness. Do more practice questions and consistently get more than 75% correct. Consistency is the key; repeated commendable performance shows that you are ready. If, when reviewing information, you find that it all looks familiar, then it's likely you know the content. Organize or join a study group. You are likely to find through discussion with others preparing to test that you are indeed knowledgeable about the content. Ask your course instructors to assess your readiness. Look over your performance on the comprehensive predictor test that you took before you graduated. See what that test indicated in terms of readiness. Your faculty should be able to provide you with some interpretation of those results.

Canceling for Good Reason

You have planned the best time to test and carefully prepared for several weeks. All of a sudden you get food poisoning, or your dog dies, or your mom calls with the unexpected news that your dad had a heart attack. What do you do? Do you go ahead with the plan? Or do you recognize that perhaps you'd be better off postponing the test until a time when you can have uninterrupted focus. No one would think that you are weak or incapable if you postpone your test. Of course, it is a financial decision too, but so is not being successful when you know you could be. Don't think that just because the money has been spent and you are supposed to test tomorrow that you must. If an unexpected event occurs that interrupts your focus, then delay–for your success.

Changing Your Appointment

If you choose to change your appointment, you must do this at least one full business day before your test is scheduled. For example, a test scheduled for 10:00 a.m. Monday must be changed by 10:00 a.m. the Friday before. There is no charge for this change. Any changes after that point will result in forfeiting the exam fee. You cannot leave a message at the testing center. You must reschedule online (www.pearsonvue.com/nclex) or by phone. If you have special accommodations, you must contact the NCLEX-RN® program coordinator, just as you did to originally schedule. If you do not arrive on time, you also forfeit your time slot and exam fee, and must register and pay again.

Eat Properly the Days Before the Test

Just as marathon runners and other athletes carefully select their meals for the days before a big event, you should take the same care. Avoid spicy or irritating foods if they are known to give you trouble. The night before the test, consider a high-carbohydrate, high-protein meal that will provide you with energy and is easily digestible. Heavy or fatty meals will digest more slowly and possibly interrupt your sleep.

One Day Before the NCLEX-RN®

Finding the Testing Center

To find the address of your testing location, go to http://www.ncsbn.org/pdfs/PPTs_072502.pdf. Get directions from www.mapquest.com or another direction web site or a software program. Testing centers may be located downtown on one-way streets or in a shopping center with many competing signs. Be sure you know where you are going ahead of time. If you arrive late, that would be a problem, so know your routes.

Special Time for You

Take a long walk, go to the movies, soak in a hot tub, or play at the park with your children. Do anything that will free your mind and help you relax before you test. Work on a painting, read a favorite book, or clean out closets. Whatever makes you feel as if you have accomplished something and leaves you feeling both satisfied and relaxed.

Caffeine, Alcohol, and Medications

Whatever you normally tolerate in the way of caffeine and alcohol, in moderation, may be alright to ingest before the test. It is definitely not the time to cut back on your caffeine intake, or to have a few drinks to relax you. Keep to your normal (light or moderate) pattern as much as possible. These stimulants can affect your performance.

Sleeping the Night Before

It is reasonable to expect that you will be nervous or excited before testing and that your sleep will be fitful. It is possible to bank sleep, so sleep well for several nights before you test and you can tolerate one night of incomplete sleep. The most important thing is to relax and not fight your emotions. However, you should avoid taking a sleeping aid. Do practice relaxation techniques, listen to soothing sounds, and deep breathe so that sleep comes more easily on a night that you definitely want a good sleep. If you awaken several times and see the alarm clock, convince yourself that you trust the alarm to awaken you and go back to sleep.

The Day of the NCLEX-RN®

Drinking Water

Water helps the brain to function. The cells operate best with appropriate hydration. Begin loading up on water the day before (just like athletes do), so that your body is properly hydrated as well as flushed of toxins. Drink water before testing, and bring a bottle of water with you for your break.

Eating Properly

You have scheduled the test for your best time of day. If you are testing in the morning, then you should eat a light breakfast, again higher in carbohydrates and protein, rather than fats. If you are someone who doesn't generally eat breakfast, you will want to consider something small to give you an energy boost and fight off the stress of the testing experience. If you test later in the day, remember to eat a light meal that is moderate in carbohydrates and high in protein. You can indulge in a big celebratory meal when you are finished with the test–perhaps that hot fudge sundae.

Gum or Candy

To avoid dry mouth or to release some tension, gum or hard candy may be helpful to you. However, in times of anxiety, you might really begin to concentrate on your gum chewing, rather than on your test. You may want to chew gum or suck hard candy up until the time testing begins, and then focus all your energy on the test itself. During the break, or when you have finished, your dry mouth might appreciate something sweet.

Snacks During the Breaks

It is advisable to bring a snack to the testing center. If you are testing long enough for the computer to provide you the first of the two preprogrammed optional breaks, then you've tested for a couple of hours. A piece of fruit, a cup of yogurt, some crackers, or a granola bar will provide you with some needed energy and help you to continue the test. If there is any delay at the testing center, then you may begin to get hungry sooner than you had expected. Having a snack with you will allow your blood sugar to stay high enough for your brain to continue to function properly.

Identification

Just as required by the airlines or customs, you must show proper identification to test. You must bring your Authorization to Test, your valid picture identification, and secondary identification with signatures to the testing center. Without this information, you won't be permitted to test. You will forfeit your testing appointment and fee for the day, and will need to reschedule and pay a testing fee again. Your fingerprint, signature, and photo will be taken at the testing center.

Your Personal Belongings

No study materials may be brought into the testing facility. You will be issued a locker for your backpack or purse. Snacks, identification, and personal-needs items can be stored in the locker. Turn off your cell phone and/or pager. No calculators will be allowed; there will be one on the computer for your use.

Testing Alone

While it is likely that you have spent your nursing program closely linked to another student, it is highly recommended that you go to the testing center alone. When you test with your friends or study partners, you may be concerned about that person if you finish first, causing undue anxiety about your performance and theirs. Or, if you finish later, then your anxiety may increase acutely and unnecessarily. Testing together can interrupt your concentration and thus affect your performance.

Reliable Transportation

Your test is considered an appointment, so make sure you are on time. An unfamiliar mass transit schedule, an unreliable car, or a scarcity of taxis can cause you to be late. Be sure that your car operates. Confirm that the taxi will come, the estimated fare, and that the driver knows the way to the testing center. If someone is driving you, then consider having that person drop you off and wait at least two hours to return. Having someone waiting outside can put added pressure on you (see Testing Alone). The only person that you should be worried about during testing is you. The testing center will not permit family or friends to wait inside or contact you for any reason during the exam.

Happy Thoughts

Find happy thoughts to occupy your mind on your way to and just before the test. While a little bit of stress is good and keeps you on your toes, a lot of stress can paralyze. Play your favorite CD on the way to the test, something that makes you feel good inside. Or say your favorite prayer that grounds you and makes you feel closer to your blessings. Bring a picture of your spouse, your children, or your inspiration to look at one last time before you go inside. Whatever you have to do to find your happy place, then do that on the way and just before the test.

During the Test

Focus and eliminate distractions. Hopefully you can choose a seat that doesn't permit you to notice the other testers, maybe one facing the back wall away from the door. Wear layered clothing so that you can adjust to the temperature of the center. Avoid bracelets or other jewelry that will get in your way or cause you to fidget. Find a familiar and comforting phrase to repeat when you become anxious. Allow yourself to doodle on the erasable board if it calms you. Watch your time – the six-hour time limit includes the tutorial, breaks, and the examination.

Item 76

The computer didn't shut off after Item 75 – what will you do? The computer obviously hasn't made a decision about your competency either way at this point. Therefore, you must continue your testing. If the computer was sure that you weren't capable, it would have definitely shut off. Now all you have to do is prove on the next several items that you are capable of bearing the title of Registered Nurse. The average number of items on any candidate's exam is about 110. Item 76 is your friend–do well.

Item 200

You are getting tired. When is this going to end? Take another deep breath. You had an optional break at 2 hours and another optional break comes at 3 1/2 hours. Refocus. Practice relaxation techniques. Hold on. If the computer was sure of your performance at this point, it would have shut off. Go for the last set of questions as if they were your first. Check the clock for the six-hour limit and pace yourself through the next items, 10 at a time. Do your best!

After the NCLEX-RN®

Plan a Reward

You've worked hard for several years now. While you have studied hard in school, you may have also experienced demands at home or work. The hard work isn't over until you've got the RN license in your hand. Plan a reward for when the test is over–a weekend at the beach, a cruise, or even a week of sleep. Simple rewards such as dinner and a movie may help as well, especially if you sense success and want some immediate gratification.

Confidentiality

When you begin the NCLEX-RN® you indicate your agreement to keep the material on the exam confidential. That means posting, sharing, or discussing the items you remember could result in legal action. Besides, the items you remember after the test are often the ones that gave you the most difficulty. There is no way you could remember them verbatim nor could you know the correct answer for certain.

Getting Your Results

Visit your State Board of Nursing website to find out the best method for getting your results. We are sure you want to know as soon as possible. Most states encourage you to go to the Board of Nursing website or to a voice response unit (telephone prompter) to enter your social security number and learn if you are listed as a Registered Nurse. Not being listed can mean that your results are not available yet, not necessarily that you were not successful. Calling the National Council office will not be helpful. All states will provide written notification of your results with appropriate documentation by ground mail. In the event you were not successful, you may retest in 45 or 91 days, depending your state.

Test Plan for the NCLEX-RN®

The NCLEX-RN® is constructed according to a test plan that provides a framework for the scope and content of the examination questions. The breadth of content is based on findings of the *2002 RN Practice Analysis*. The NCLEX-RN® includes application-based scenarios in the clinical areas of medical-surgical, maternity, pediatrics, and mental health nursing. Several additional concepts and processes fundamental to the safe and effective practice at the entry level are integrated into NCLEX-RN®, including:

- Nursing process
- Caring
- Communication skills
- Cultural awareness
- Documentation
- Disaster management
- End-of-life care
- Principles of teaching/learning
- Error prevention
- Community resources
- Lifespan approach
- Gerontologic considerations
- Family systems

The scope of the test encompasses data from the most recent practice analysis. The test content includes clinical situations in medical, surgical, obstetric, pediatric, and mental health nursing. The categories are collectively referred to as "Client Needs"—a comprehensive classification system to define nursing actions and competencies across all settings for all clients. The items on the NCLEX-RN® itself are distributed according to established percentages among four major categories of Client Needs:

Safe, Effective Care Environment	
• Management of care	13-19%
• Safety and infection control	8-14%
Health Promotion and Maintenance	6-12%
Psychosocial Integrity	6-12%
Physiological Integrity	
• Basic care and comfort	6-12%
• Pharmacological and parenteral therapies	13-19%
• Reduction of risk potential	13-19%
• Physiological adaptation	11-17%

The majority of items are written at the application or higher levels of cognitive ability (which requires more complex thought processing). The average reading level for the exam is 10th grade. The NCLEX-RN® is not intended to test the ability of the candidate to read, but to determine the level of proficiency in understanding nursing concepts and activities.

The table on the following pages demonstrates the NCLEX-RN® Test Plan as it utilizes the four major categories of Client Needs. The percentage of items is based on the results of the practice analysis study and judgment from a panel of experts.

Items in the NCLEX-RN® Test Plan are not limited exclusively to the examples on the following pages. More specific information and publications on test content are available from the National Council of State Boards of Nursing, Inc., 111 E. Wacker Drive, Suite 2900, Chicago, IL 60601 or at www.ncsbn.org. The following processes are integrated throughout the four major Client Needs categories as they are fundamental to the practice of nursing:

- **Nursing Process**– a scientific problem-solving approach to client care that includes assessment, analysis, planning, implementation, and evaluation.
- **Caring**– interaction of the nurse and client in an atmosphere of mutual respect and trust. In this collaborative environment, the nurse provides hope, support, and compassion to help achieve desired outcomes.
- **Communication and Documentation**– verbal and nonverbal interactions between the nurse and the client, the client's significant others and the other members of the health care team. Events and activities associated with client care are validated in written or electronic records that reflect quality and accountability in the provision of care.
- **Teaching/Learning**– facilitation of the acquisition of knowledge, skills, and attitudes promoting a change in behavior.

NCLEX-RN® Test Plan — Table of Client Needs Categories

<table>
<tr><th colspan="2">Client Needs</th></tr>
<tr><th colspan="2">Safe, Effective Care Environment</th></tr>
<tr><td rowspan="2">Management of Care
13% - 19%</td><td>Examples of Related Content</td></tr>
<tr><td>
• Advanced directives
• Advocacy
• Case management
• Client rights
• Collaboration with multidisciplinary team
• Concepts of management
• Confidentiality
• Consultation
• Continuity of care
• Delegation
• Establishing priorities
• Ethical practice
• Informed consent
• Legal rights and responsibilities
• Performance improvement
• Referrals
• Resource management
• Staff education
• Supervision
</td></tr>
<tr><td colspan="2">Test Item Topics</td></tr>
<tr><td colspan="2">
• Using community resources
• Monitoring a staff member's performance
• Documenting client care, and responses to care appropriately
• Practicing nursing using ethical principles
• Understanding the nurse's legal responsibilities for the delivery of care, and identifying professional practice limitations (e.g., refusing to perform tasks not specified in nursing practice laws, rules or regulations)
• Assigning to, delegating to, or supervising delivery of care by other members of the health care team
• Reporting to other health care team members
• Identifying and reporting physical or sexual abuse to adult and/or child
• Assessing, organizing, and prioritizing care for assigned group of clients
• Reporting a health care provider's unsafe practice activities (improper care, substance abuse, inappropriate words/actions to clients or families)
• Informing a client of rights (e.g., advanced directives, confidentiality of information, consent for treatment)
• Participating in quality assurance activities
• Preparing a variance report or irregular occurrence/incident report
• Providing information to help a client make an informed decision regarding treatment options
• Participating in education of staff, clients, and client care providers
• Evaluating the outcomes of care provided by others
</td></tr>
</table>

Test Item Topics: Management of Care (continued)

- Notifying other health care team members about changes in client's status
- Implementing verbal/phone orders
- Respecting client's control of personal space or property
- Using cost-efficient method for delivery of nursing care
- Acting as an advocate for client needs, rights, and best care
- Collaborating with other members of the health care team about the plan and delivery of client care
- Planning an interdisciplinary plan for client care using relevant and current findings in the nursing/health care literature
- Communicating relevant findings regarding client care to the appropriate member of the health care team (laboratory data, assessment findings, client issues, unclear physician orders)
- Participating in the discharge planning process
- Protecting client privacy (bodily exposure, collection of health history, communication of personal information)
- Coordinating transfer of client to another setting/facility
- Initiating a consultation or referral to other members of the health care team
- Acting as a professional resource to others on the health care team
- Using an organized method (clinical pathways, care maps, or care plans) to plan and evaluate client care
- Assessing a client's/family's knowledge about advance directives and providing support for their decision-making process

Client Needs

Safe, Effective Care Environment

<table>
<tr><td rowspan="2">Safety and Infection Control
8% - 14%</td><td>Examples of Related Content</td></tr>
<tr><td>• Accident prevention
• Disaster planning
• Emergency response plan
• Error prevention
• Handling hazardous and infectious materials
• Home safety
• Injury prevention
• Medical and surgical asepsis
• Reporting of incident/event/ irregular occurrence/variance
• Safe use of equipment
• Standard/transmission-based/ other precautions
• Use of restraints/ safety devices
• Security Plan</td></tr>
</table>

Test Item Topics

- Operating and maintaining equipment safely, such as the operation of an infusion pump
- Preventing falls and accidents by providing appropriate assistive devices
- Practicing the principles of infection control—implementing interventions to prevent infection and promote healing
- Teaching the client and family ways to prevent infection; transmission of infection and contamination to others
- Identifying clients at risk for infection/superinfection
- Reporting communicable diseases
- Applying restraints safely with use of least-restrictive devices, until no longer needed
- Documenting the client's response to the use of restraints
- Adhering to standard procedure for handling biohazardous materials
- Maintaining medical/surgical asepsis as needed
- Preparing and implementing internal/external disaster plans
- Checking the accuracy of orders
- Verifying the identity of a client
- Identifying a client's allergies and documenting this on the medical record
- Implementing measures to protect the immunosuppressed client
- Assessing and modifying the health care and home environment for potential hazards or sources of injury
- Participating in health screening program for the detection of illness
- Determining the level of mobility and motor skills for self-care and activities of daily living

Test Item Topics: Safety and Infection Control (continued)
• Assessing the client's level of sensory perception • Providing visual or auditory aids to promote independence and sufficient self-care • Adhering to unit/hospital policy for standards of care • Double-checking unfamiliar medications, narcotics, or unusually small or large doses with another nurse

Client Needs

Health Promotion and Maintenance

<table>
<tr><td rowspan="2">Percentage of Test
6% - 12%</td><td>Examples of Related Content</td></tr>
<tr><td>• Aging process
• Antepartum, intrapartum, postpartum, and newborn
• Developmental stages and transitions
• Disease prevention
• Expected body image changes
• Family planning
• Family systems
• Growth and development
• Health and wellness
• Health promotion programs
• Health screening
• High-risk behaviors
• Human sexuality
• Immunizations
• Lifestyle choices
• Principles of teaching/learning
• Self-care
• Techniques of physical assessment</td></tr>
<tr><td colspan="2">Test Item Topics</td></tr>
<tr><td colspan="2">• Identifying signs of potential complications of pregnancy
• Monitoring a client in labor
• Detecting non-reassuring fetal heart pattern on external monitoring
• Providing normal newborn care, including circumcision care, cord care, and infant nutrition
• Teaching infant care to care providers
• Assessing a newborn for potential complications
• Providing care to client following delivery
• Promoting positive and effective parenting skills through family education
• Integrating age-related variations, and considering life transitions into care plan, and providing care in light of those considerations
• Choosing developmentally appropriate diversional activities for the hospitalized child
• Communicating with the client and family in a developmentally and culturally appropriate manner
• Discussing sexuality issues with respect, and in the appropriate environment
• Modifying the sensory environment for the aging adult as needed
• Respecting cultural beliefs and personal lifestyle choices by providing non-judgmental care
• Helping a client to use nonpharmacologic pain management during labor
• Evaluating the client's ability to provide safe care to a newborn in the home environment</td></tr>
</table>

Test Item Topics: Health Promotion and Maintenance (continued)

- Obtaining pertinent information about the client's lifestyle patterns and health-related issues
- Measuring baseline physical data and reporting abnormal findings, including vital signs, laboratory data, and height and weight
- Planning and/or participating in health promotion programs, such as smoking cessation, weight management, stress management, and immunization for children and adults
- Encouraging client participation in health screening programs for breast cancer, hypertension, cervical cancer, prostate cancer, and inborn metabolic or hematologic disorders in the newborn
- Assisting the client and family to identify and modify sources of potential injury in the home environment
- Determining clients at risk for alterations in health or injury
- Identifying alternative practices for healing used by the client and family
- Assessing body systems and daily functions for early physical manifestations of illness
- Providing information about immunization schedules, and evaluating the adequacy and timeliness of child and adult immunization
- Teaching self-examination screening techniques (breast, testicular, and skin mapping)
- Interpreting skin test results
- Evaluating the client/family ability to meet health care needs in performing activities of daily living in the home environment (bowel elimination, feeding, ambulation, bathing, sleep)
- Involving the client/family in goal-setting and care-planning activities
- Identifying noncompliance in the client receiving health care
- Identifying the client's/family's cultural beliefs regarding health practices, lifestyle, diet, sleep, exercise, and medicine
- Integrating alternative or homeopathic healing modalities into the health promotion
- Adjusting teaching strategies and approach to care to meet the developmental, cognitive, emotional, cultural and spiritual needs of the client/family
- Evaluating client response to traditional and alternative health care interventions

Client Needs

Psychosocial Integrity

<table>
<tr><td rowspan="2">Percentage of Test
6% - 12%</td><td colspan="2">Examples of Related Content</td></tr>
<tr><td>• Abuse and neglect
• Behavioral interventions
• Chemical dependency
• Coping mechanisms
• Crisis intervention
• Cultural diversity
• End of life
• Family dynamics
• Grief and loss
• Mental illness concepts
• Psychopathology</td><td>• Religious and spiritual influences on health
• Sensory or perceptual alterations
• Situational role changes
• Stress management
• Support systems
• Therapeutic communication
• Therapeutic environment
• Unexpected body image changes</td></tr>
<tr><td colspan="3">Test Item Topics</td></tr>
<tr><td colspan="3">• Assessing the adequacy of support for home care of the client
• Utilizing family support systems for home care and coping
• Identifying the pattern of interaction and function within the client's support system
• Actively listening to clients verbalize concerns and fear
• Communicating therapeutically with client, family, and staff
• Supporting a terminally ill client/family through the grieving process
• Integrating the client's spiritual needs into the delivery of care
• Enhancing positive coping styles of the client and family
• Facilitating role adaptation related to health status or developmental stage
• Using alternative methods to communicate with the client who has impaired sensory function
• Interpreting the reasons for a client's noncompliance with the treatment plan
• Aiding the client in adjusting to changes in body image
• Assessing the client's response to illness and treatment
• Assisting the client to identify sources of stress in life situations as they relate to health
• Establishing a trust relationship and open rapport with the client and family
• Implementing crisis intervention techniques as needed
• Assessing the client/family emotional reactions to illness/injury and change in individual, family, and societal roles</td></tr>
</table>

Test Item Topics: Psychosocial Integrity (continued)

- Encouraging the use of constructive, problem-solving skills and critical thinking
- Modeling a positive attitude, feeling of hope, and healthy perspective for coping and adaptation
- Appreciating the client/family uniqueness in dealing with pain, illness, alterations in lifestyle, role, and activities
- Identifying signs of physical, sexual or emotional abuse, and neglect of the client or family
- Detecting physical and behavioral indicators of substance abuse and dependency
- Promoting verbal and non-verbal activities indicating positive self-esteem
- Identifying a client with an eating disorder
- Implementing interventions to assist client with mental illness in controlling behavior
- Assessing the client's orientation to person, time, place, and situation
- Implementing measures to maximize independence in the client with alterations in sensory or cognitive status
- Maintaining the function and safety of the client with dementia or delusions
- Minimizing and establishing limits for undesirable behavior, disruptive, or destructive behaviors
- Communicating with the client in a therapeutic manner
- Reporting high-risk situations for injury to client, family, staff, or others
- Evaluating the client's perception of the physical and situational environment
- Determining the client's responsiveness to behavioral, pharmacologic, or other treatment approaches
- Minimizing undesirable, disruptive, or destructive behaviors
- Observing the client for evidence of potential self-injury
- Evaluating the ability of the client with mental health illness to function independently with safety to self and others
- Responding therapeutically to inappropriate behavior, gestures, and verbal remarks
- Providing education to client/family about electroconvulsant therapy, and the physical and psychologic effects
- Facilitating client/family participation in individual family/group therapy

Client Needs

Physiological Integrity

	Examples of Related Content
Basic Care and Comfort 6% - 12%	• Alternative and complementary therapies • Assistive devices • Elimination • Mobility or immobility • Nonpharmacological comfort interventions • Nutrition and oral hydration • Palliative/comfort care • Personal hygiene • Rest and sleep

Test Item Topics

- Assessing the client's nutritional and hydration status
- Assisting the client with selecting and consuming healthy food
- Assisting with ambulation, feeding, hygiene, and dressing as needed
- Administering tube feedings safely
- Recording intake and output data as needed
- Promoting methods for normal urinary and bowel elimination
- Administering an enema for diagnostic or therapeutic purposes
- Providing care to stoma while maintaining good skin integrity at the stomal site
- Inserting intermittent or indwelling urinary catheter properly
- Implementing measures to promote healthy skin integrity and prevent pressure-related injury to the skin
- Providing care and maintaining safety for the client receiving conscious sedation
- Identifying common and adverse side effects of drug therapy, including chemotherapy
- Demonstrating understanding about the use of and precautions for drugs the client receives
- Teaching clients how to self-administer nonprescription medications
- Educating clients when to report adverse effects related to medication to the health care provider
- Reconstituting powdered medications

Client Needs

Physiological Integrity

	Examples of Related Content
Pharmacological and Parenteral Therapies 13% - 19%	• Adverse effects/contraindications and side effects • Blood and blood products • Central venous access devices • Dosage calculation • Expected outcomes/effects • Intravenous therapy • Medication administration • Pharmacological actions • Pharmacological interactions • Pharmacological pain management • Total parenteral nutrition • Parenteral fluids

Test Item Topics

- Withholding medications when appropriate
- Inserting a peripheral intravenous catheter
- Evaluating the client's need for PRN dosing of medication
- Determining, monitoring and intervening appropriately as to a client's response to administered medications, including adverse reactions to blood product (blood transfusion), fluid, parenteral nutrition or medication
- Properly calculating infusion rates
- Disposing of unused portions of controlled substances using appropriate hospital policy
- Implementing and teaching the client/family to perform exercises to maximize the client's range of motion and prevent contractures
- Teaching client and family to safely use assistive devices to increase mobility
- Providing post-mortem care
- Administering medication via oral, nasogastric, topical, subcutaneous, intramuscular, intravenous, conjunctival, buccal, nasal, or rectal routes
- Providing care to intravenous or intra-arterial devices and the site
- Assessing intravascular sites for complications related to indwelling catheters
- Monitoring the rate of infusion and possible complications related to intermittent or continuous solutions
- Providing measures for pain relief and comfort using non-pharmacologic measures
- Instructing the client and family in holistic methods to control pain and promote rest and sleep at home or in the hospitalized setting
- Determining a need for range of motion exercises

Client Needs

Physiological Integrity

<table>
<tr><td rowspan="2">Reduction of Risk Potential 13% - 19%</td><td>Examples of Related Content</td></tr>
<tr><td>

- Diagnostic tests
- Laboratory values
- Monitoring conscious sedation
- Potential for complications of diagnostic tests/treatments/procedures
- Potential for complications from surgical procedures and health alterations
- Therapeutic procedures
- Vital signs
- Potential for Alterations in Body Systems
- System Specific Assessments

</td></tr>
<tr><td colspan="2">Test Item Topics</td></tr>
<tr><td colspan="2">

- Monitoring results of diagnostic and laboratory data
- Maintaining skin integrity
- Implementing interventions to promote respiratory function and prevent complications, such as atelectasis, pneumonia, pneumothorax
- Implementing interventions to prevent circulatory complications related to immobility, surgery, pregnancy, or special procedures, such as thrombophlebitis, bleeding, tamponade, or poor perfusion
- Performing nursing activities to prevent neurologic complications related to change in consciousness, foot drop, and palsy
- Monitoring for signs of altered sensorium, increased intracranial pressure, change in mentation or mood, diminished or increased perception of pain, and altered sensorioperceptual integrity
- Promoting optimum venous return using positioning techniques, thromboembolic stockings, ambulation, and elevation of lower extremities
- Correctly collecting specimens of bodily fluids, tissue, blood, or drainage for accurate diagnostic evaluation of the client's health problem
- Implementing measures to prevent gastrointestinal distress, such as nausea, vomiting, diarrhea, reflux, constipation, cramping, impaired motility, poor intestinal absorption, or aspiration
- Providing care to maximize client's mobility
- Monitoring the respiratory function after the use of anesthesia, including the use of pulse oximetry
- Assessing the quality of breath sounds, work of breathing, and respiratory excursions
- Detecting poor pacemaker function

</td></tr>
</table>

Test Item Topics: Physiological Integrity (continued)

- Interpreting ECG patterns indicative of dysrhythmia or risk for cardiac emergency
- Preventing infection of indwelling objects, such as urinary catheters, intravenous lines, tracheal tubes, PEG tubes, PIC lines, and chest tubes
- Performing blood glucose checks
- Monitoring change in vital signs from baseline
- Emphasizing the importance of cancer screening
- Teaching the client and family to apply sun protectants for skin exposure
- Evaluating wound healing
- Assessing the client for adverse effects related to chemotherapy
- Providing cast care that includes assessment for neurovascular compromise
- Monitoring the patency, function and effectiveness of tubes, drains, and other indwelling lines
- Collecting specimens of bodily fluid, blood, stool, using correct technique, labeling, storage and transportation
- Notifying the primary care provider of deviations in health status, laboratory data, or blood gas information from the normal range or baseline

Client Needs

Physiological Integrity

	Examples of Related Content	
Physiological Adaptation 11% - 17%	• Alterations in body systems • Fluid and electrolyte imbalance • Hemodynamics • Illness management • Infectious diseases	• Medical emergencies • Pathophysiology • Radiation therapy • Unexpected response to therapies

Test Item Topics

- Demonstrating understanding of the basic pathophysiology related to the client's health disorder
- Describing the cause of illness as it affects the client's health
- Describing the effects of chronic disease on multiple organ systems
- Understanding how various disease processes reduce the client's overall health and activities of daily living
- Performing cardiopulmonary resuscitation
- Identifying a client's need for oxygen
- Providing respiratory care to the client receiving mechanical ventilation
- Providing care to the client requiring a tracheostomy
- Providing care to the client with a chest tube
- Minimizing the effects of poisoning
- Administering phototherapy for elevated bilirubin in newborns
- Providing care to the client receiving traction devices
- Responding expediently and appropriately to the client experiencing choking or respiratory distress
- Providing care to the client with burn injury
- Promoting homeostasis with fluid and electrolyte monitoring
- Responding expediently and decisively to the client with active bleeding
- Providing care to the client experiencing seizures
- Detecting electrolyte and acid-base imbalance through the interpretation of laboratory data and physical assessment
- Assessing the client for adverse effects related to radiation therapy
- Providing emergency care for clients with injury/trauma
- Using immobilizing devices correctly
- Providing information to facilitate a client's decision making
- Reporting client-based changes and communicating relevant information about the client/family as part of the shift report

Test Item Topics: Physiological Integrity (continued)
• Checking the accuracy of client orders • Assessing the client for risk, or physical indications, of infection • Participating in hemo/peritoneal dialysis or other special treatment as indicated • Applying heat/cold therapy appropriately

Developing the NCLEX-RN®

The current NCLEX-RN® was developed using a three-phase process. A 10-member panel of subject matter experts created a list of nursing activities typically performed by new nurses. This list was developed into a survey instrument that was sent to 4000 Registered Nurses licensed from March to May 2002. The surveys were distributed in October 2002. Of the surveys that were returned by November 2002, 1317 were analyzed in order to develop the current test plan. The nurses who participated in this study represented nursing practice geographically, ethnically, and by age, gender, and type of nursing program. The practice analysis included nurses who were not educated in the United States. About half indicated work experience as a nursing assistant and almost a quarter indicated work experience as a licensed practical/vocational nurse.

The 137 nursing activities on the survey were ranked by frequency of the activity in the work setting and the priority for clinical care of clients. These rankings were used to revise the test plan and assign test items to it. Items are developed with great care by a team of practicing nurses and are reviewed by a second team of practicing nurses to be sure they reflect current nursing practice. Items that become outdated due to changes in nursing practice are deleted from the item bank. Each candidate receives 15 new items within the first 75 items of each test. Since you will not be able to identify which items are new, it is important to address every item with equal attention and detail. In the event that you must retest, the items that were on previous tests will not appear again in subsequent tests.

The exam uses Computerized Adapted Testing (CAT) to distribute the test items. The difficulty of the item you receive is based on your success on the previous item. For example, if you get an item correct, the questions become more difficult. If you get it wrong, the questions become easier. The idea is for you to demonstrate a pattern of competency in answering the more difficult items. Since items are targeted to ability, fewer items are needed to produce test results that are stable. It is expected that you will only answer about 50% of the questions correctly, so you will want to establish that pattern of competency early and maintain it. For more detailed descriptions of CAT, please refer to the Candidate Bulletin at www.ncsbn.org/pdfs/Web_Bulletin_05.pdf.

Test-Taking Strategies

Reading Test Items

The amount of information in the item can be overwhelming and the responses can confuse you. It is best to read the stem of the question, develop a pool of answers from your total body of knowledge, then search through the responses for the one response that was in your pool of answers.

The Right Answer Is Not There

When reading the responses to an item, your first choice may not be there. Since the NCLEX-RN® expects you to know the best answer, the responses may list the second or third choice as the expected answer. This is why you need a pool of answers from which to draw. Haphazard guessing can be disastrous as there is only a 25% chance that you will guess correctly.

There Are Two Right Answers

You probably said this a few times while in the nursing program. You've got it narrowed down to two responses you think are correct. Before selecting the best response, reread the stem of the item and be sure you know what the item is asking. For the standard four-option multiple choice questions, the writers and reviewers intend for only one answer to be correct. Answers are either right or wrong. No item is keyed for two responses.

Cannot Find the Answer You Like

If, after narrowing down your choices to two and rereading the stem, you still cannot find an answer you like, you must select one and move on. Every item must be answered in order to move ahead in the test. While there is no penalty for guessing, there is reward in narrowing down the responses and giving it your best shot. Try not to stay on an item you're unsure of for more than your allotted minute. It could disrupt your thinking and make it hard to get back on track.

Finding the Pattern

There are many myths circulating about the NCLEX-RN®, such as certain preselected candidates will get 265 items or, when in doubt, choose answer C. These myths (and more) are addressed on the Candidate page at www.ncsbn.org. There are no patterns for correct answers–an equal number of As, Bs, Cs, and Ds are used as item responses. There has also been speculation that if, for example, you miss a renal question, you will get a dozen more like it. In reality, you tend to remember the items you don't know, so it only seems that these kinds of items continue to appear. There is no pattern of topics–the test items must follow the distribution of the test plan.

Priority-Setting Items

To answer a priority item (i.e., "Which one will you do first?"), you must recognize that it is likely that all four responses are correct and represent actions you would take. However, you can only choose one of these options, so you must choose the **one and only one** action that you would do before you get called out of the room for an hour. Using this cue, you can generally identify the priority action. Example: Many areas should be assessed on a postoperative client – pain, incision, drains, IV, bleeding, vital signs, level of consciousness, etc. The **one and only one** action to take, if you must choose, would be vital signs, as this would provide you with an overall assessment of the client's current status.

Client Assignment Items

When answering a client assignment item, you will find that all four clients need your attention. However, you can only choose one of these options. So you must choose the client who is the least stable or will be in trouble first (or is likely to die first) if you don't attend to the care. Using this cue, you can generally identify the priority client.

Use Clinical Reasoning

If you have never heard of the medication in the item, it may not matter. For example, the item tells you the medication is causing nausea and vomiting. What do you do for any client who is nauseous after taking a medication? Giving medication with food often helps. When in doubt, use your clinical reasoning skills to lead you to the correct response. Of course, you'll always want to look up the medication the first chance you get after testing.

What is the Question Asking?

Be sure you recognize who is the subject of the question: the client, the family, or the nurse. Also recognize that you are the Registered Nurse in most questions. If the question refers to a co-worker, you are the one delegating to RNs, or to licensed practical (vocational) nurses, and nursing assistants. Be familiar with the nursing assistant role as it differs from the nurse tech role that you may have experienced.

Using Maslow's Hierarchy

Remember that Maslow's physiologic needs represent air, water, and food; safety and security needs come next. When prioritizing, these first two levels will be helpful. For example, all the answers could not be airway, so consider sickle cell, where hydration is of utmost importance. While improving self-esteem is possible, meeting love and belonging or self-actualization needs are generally not possible in the nurse-client relationship.

Answer Changers Beware

In your test-taking experience, you may have changed the correct answer to a wrong answer because you second-guessed yourself. As a strong nurse, you should exercise sound reasoning, but not underestimate your abilities.

The NCLEX-RN® Hospital

If a supply or piece of equipment is included in the item, then consider it available for your use. If a medication is included, expect that it is in the formulary and there is an order. Also, there is no such thing as being short staffed in the NCLEX-RN® hospital; nurses always have time to sit at eye level with clients and listen to them.

The Study Calendar

Prepare a study calendar that includes days for practice tests, studying content, working and resting. Take off from work the three days prior to the exam so that you are focused and aren't thinking about yesterday's client during testing. Having fun the day before will help you to relax and allow you to access the content when you need it.

Sunday	Monday	Tuesday	Wednesday	Thursday	Friday	Saturday
Scheduled on the Web						
	Rest	Rest	Rest & Fun	NCLEX-RN®	FUN!	Rest

Study Days vs. Testing Days

The more practice you have responding to items correctly, the better prepared you will be to take the NCLEX-RN®. When you are practicing answering items–100 at a sitting–make a list of all the content that you do not know well. Use your study days to look up any content that you did not know. Use testing days to develop your rhythm for responding to test questions.

Too Slow or Too Fast

Items are designed to take about one minute each, especially if you read the item, create a pool of answers, then select the correct response. If you find that you are too slow or too fast (i.e., less than 6 minutes or greater than 14 minutes for 10 items) then break up the test into 10-item sections and work on getting a greater percentage correct (at least 70%) in 10 minutes. Once you have achieved that, move on to 20 items in 20 minutes (with at least 75% correct); then 30 items in 30 minutes and so on.

What Should I Score on Practice Tests

Since you are not expected to score 100% on the NCLEX-RN®, it is unrealistic to expect you to score 100% on the practice tests. However, you should aim for 75% to 80% on your practice tests as you develop your rhythm and get your timing down to about one minute per question.

Alternate Items

While only about 2%-3% of the average 110 items on the NCLEX-RN® exam are alternate items, it is helpful to be familiar with this style of non-multiple-choice format before taking the test. The tutorial will help you with this. There are three types of alternate-item formats. The tutorial will help you with this. Two new alternate item types were introduced in January 2005. These include a drag and drop feature asking you to put the steps in order of importance and a chart of information to read in order to respond to an item. There are also three other types of alternate-item formats. Type 1 is fill-in-the-blank, often a calculation requiring you to list an amount as a response. The unit of measure will already be in the item for you. You may also be asked to put several steps in order. Your response will be to show the correct order: for example, 5 3 4 1 2. Type 2 is a hot-spot item. You will be asked to use your computer mouse to select the zone that accurately reflects the correct response. Only one zone will be the correct response. Type 3 is a multiple response item. Six responses will be available and you will select from two to six of them. You must choose all the responses that apply; no partial credit is given for getting the item half right. Practicing alternate items before testing will be helpful so that your rhythm will not be disrupted when a new kind of question suddenly appears on the screen.

Best Wishes from ATI

If you have pursued a diligent plan for your NCLEX-RN® study throughout your nursing program, you will go into the licensure exam equipped for success. The ATI Content Mastery Series™ review modules, online testing, ATI-PLAN™ DVD series, and results from diagnostic assessments, are designed to support you in your preparation and provide you with the review materials you need to pass. Use the materials on a consistent basis. Go into the NCLEX-RN® with strength and confidence. Success is within your grasp.

Ready... Set-Registered Nurse!

References

National Council of State Boards of Nursing (2004). *NCLEX Examination Candidate Bulletin.* Retrieved January 11, 2004, from www.ncsbn.org.

Smith, J. & Crawford, L. (2003). *Report of Findings from the 2002 RN Practice Analysis Linking the NCLEX-RN® to Practice.* Chicago: National Council of State Boards of Nursing.

A Word from an NCLEX-RN® Survivor

Looking back on my days as a nursing student brings many fond memories to mind. As a student, everything is scary. Even things that I knew I could do were still scary. I had to transfer everything I did in lab with my classmates over to a real live client. My client's eyes would always drift right to the NURSING STUDENT badge I was wearing along with the scrubs with the insignia of my school on them. And in an instant, my confidence level dropped. They knew I was practicing on them. They knew I was nervous. I would look at the licensed RNs taking report and think, "If only I could be one of them," as they looked at me thinking, "Oh no, not another student." But at least I had my fellow students with me. We were all in the same boat. We would give each other the support and the courage we needed to come back the next day, and the day after that.

Then before I knew it, we were graduating. This meant the next step was NCLEX®. I scheduled my test, trying to pick the best day and time. I thought, "Should I schedule it early so that my mind would be fresh, or maybe late in the day so I'd have time to review some last-minute notes?" I finally decided on a time and day, and the countdown began: 14 days til NCLEX®, 13 days til NCLEX®. I reviewed notes. I quizzed fellow classmates. I watched ER, paying attention to every drug they were yelling out to push STAT, hoping I knew why. I told everyone in my life not to talk to me or expect anything from me until after NCLEX®. Only one day to NCLEX®. I followed all the instructions given to me: no exotic foods, no staying up late, no alcohol, and I went to bed. I woke up the next morning with a sick feeling. The only thing consoling me was that six hours from now the test-taking anxiety would be over. After proving to the testing center three different ways, including fingerprints, that I was indeed Lisa R. Davila, I sat down to begin. Seventy-five questions and it should turn off. Seventy-five questions and it should turn off. Why am I on the 78th question????? I start to panic, thinking I am failing miserably. Then at 80, it shuts off. I am instantly mad. I should have gotten more questions to prove how smart I am. But it is over. And I am numb. Two days later, after convincing myself I had failed and deciding I want nothing more to do with health care and I will just work at The Gap, I get my results. I had passed. I was a Registered Nurse.

Now that I have been a licensed RN for almost a year, the things that scared me in nursing school do not anymore. No longer does my heart race when an IV infiltrates. I do not break out in a cold sweat when I have to page a doctor. When I ask clients if they have any questions, I don't hope the answer is no. I am now able to talk with my clients while I am hanging their IV fluids. I can explain procedures to families without having to look up the information. I am able to look at the big picture instead of focusing on each and every detail. And when students are on my floor, I welcome them with open arms because I know that they are the future of nursing. I look forward to challenges now because I am comfortable with the basics. Nursing school was all about the tasks. Being a Registered Nurse is all about the clients. And that is what I love.

Lisa R. Davila, RN, BSN